Learning in the Early Years

KT-574-601

Photocopiable activities for

Mathematics

Ann Montague-Smith

Author
Ann Montague-Smith

Editor
Sally Gray

Assistant editor
Clare Miller

Series designer
Joy White

Designer
Claire Belcher

Illustrations
Sami Sweeten

Cover photo
Martyn Chillmaid

Published by Scholastic Ltd, Villiers House, Clarendon Avenue,
Leamington Spa, Warwickshire CV32 5PR

© 1998 Scholastic Ltd   Text © 1998 Ann Montague-Smith
1 2 3 4 5 6 7 8 9 0   8 9 0 1 2 3 4 5 6 7

British Library Cataloguing-in-Publication Data
A catalogue record for this book is available from the British Library.

ISBN 0-590-53879-9

Contents

Introduction

The *Learning in the Early Years – Mathematics Photocopiable Activity Book* contains forty-eight activities suitable for children aged three-to-five years. The activities use materials which are widely available in playgroups, nurseries and reception classes.

The Desirable Outcomes for Mathematics

Each chapter in this book deals with a different area of the Desirable Outcomes for Mathematics as specified by the School Curriculum and Assessment Authority in their publication *Desirable Outcomes for Children's Learning*. The ideas can also be applied equally well to the pre-school curriculum guidance documents for Wales, Scotland and Northern Ireland. The chapters are:
- Chapter one – 'Counting' – these activities will help to develop the skills which children need in order to be confident and consistent in their counting. These skills form the basis of all the number-based learning which follows once children begin school at five years of age.

- Chapter two – 'Number' – children will benefit from using these activities alongside those in the 'Counting' chapter. This will help them to be able to use their understanding of numbers, to read and write numerals, and to begin to add and subtract using objects in real-life situations.
- Chapter three – 'Pattern' – this is the foundation of algebra. The enjoyable activities in this chapter will help children to understand what makes a pattern and to describe and copy patterns as well as make their own.
- Chapter four – 'Sorting, matching and comparing' – these activities help children to begin to understand measuring, a vital life-skill. They will learn about balancing, comparing and ordering and sequencing events, to help them to make sense of the world around them and its events.
- Chapter five – 'Shape and space' – young children enjoy finding out how things join together and come apart. These activities provide motivating contexts for the children to learn about and explore the properties of 2D and 3D shapes.

Throughout the book there is an emphasis on investigation and problem solving. All the activities are intended to develop mathematical language and its use.

How to use the photocopiable activities

The photocopiable activities are designed to be adaptable to provide a flexible resource. Enlarging some of the activity sheets to A3-size can often be beneficial, providing bigger games to use and helping those children who have difficulty in manipulating small objects. Pasting the sheets to card also adds to their durability. Likewise, colouring the sheets adds to their visual appeal.

Make multiple copies of an activity sheet so that children can use a number of copies where there are a variety of activity possibilities.

Encourage children to work in pairs and groups so that they can share their ideas. This way of working offers excellent opportunities for language development as children are encouraged to discuss their ideas for how to complete the activity.

The activity sheets can be used as records for assessment. Add the completed sheets to portfolios of evidence of achievement. They can be used to assess the children's mathematical knowledge, skills and understanding.

Where there are children with Special Educational Needs (SEN) adapt the activities to suit the child's needs. Where a child has a physical disability, provide suitable resources to be used with the activity sheet. Where a child is a slow learner, provide extra support and encouragement by discussing the activity with the child until the child is confident.

Using resources

Some of the activities require other resources to be used alongside the activity sheet. These resources have been specially chosen because they are to be found in most playgroup, nursery or reception classes, such as dice, sand and water play materials, colouring and painting equipment and so on. Some of the number activities require numeral cards. These cards can be home-made or purchased, and if stored carefully will last for many years.

Working with parents

Sheets can be sent home for children and parents to do together or to inform parents of the things that the children are doing at your group. Choose sheets to go home which can be supported by items readily available in most homes, such as buttons or pennies for counting and making patterns, scissors, pencils, coloured crayons, dice, and playing cards which can be used as numeral cards. Display information about the topics which children are covering on a notice board or in an information sheet. This can also include help and advice for using the activity sheets which are sent home.

How to use this book

This book supports and extends the ideas covered in its sister book – *Learning in the Early Years – Mathematics*. When choosing a concept or skill to teach from the first book, look for support and extension material in this book. This will enhance the children's learning. Activities are arranged in a similar order to the first book. Where appropriate, the concept and skill development is the same or an extension of what is included in the first book. You can either use this activity book in conjunction with the first book or it can stand alone as a useful activity resource for your mathematics curriculum.

About this series

In the *Learning in the Early Years* series there are six books to cover each of the Desirable Outcomes for learning: 'Personal and Social Development', 'Language and Literacy', 'Mathematics', 'Knowledge and Understanding of the World', 'Physical Development' and 'Creative Development'. Each of these books covers planning, assessment and record-keeping and provides activities designed to cover all of the Desirable Outcomes for that subject. Each has a sister publication such as this one with further photocopiable activity ideas. A further book in the series *Ready for Inspection* provides guidance for management issues and advice for delivering the Desirable Outcomes effectively.

chapter one

Counting

Being able to count is essential to mathematical development. The activities in this chapter will help to develop the skills which children need for effective counting. The photocopiable activities can be used again and again, with different ranges of numbers, such as numbers to four, then seven, then ten and beyond.

PAGE 9

Matching
Learning objective
To match for quantity.
What to do
Work with a group of four or five children. Provide each child with some counters and a copy of the sheet. Ask the children to place a counter on each item and then to count how many. Ask questions such as: Which has five? More than two? Fewer than four? When the children are confident with how many in each set they can draw a matching set in the recording boxes.

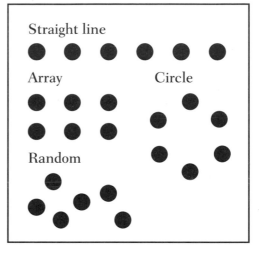

PAGE 10

Who has more?
Learning objective
To make comparisons of quantity.
What to do
Put out some shells, small bricks or counters for four children. Ask them to take a few shells and to count how many they have. Ask questions such as: Who has four? Who has more/fewer than four? Who has most/least? The activity can be repeated for different quantities. When children are confident with using the language of 'more' they can complete the sheet. Ask them to count how many they have drawn.

PAGE 11

Count and count again
Learning objective
To count the same items in different arrangements.
What to do
Work with a group of four children and ask them to count out six counters. Ask them to put the counters into different arrangements and to count each time. Change the quantity of counters and repeat the activity. Use the

photocopiable sheet to record. Write the quantity onto the sheet and let the children record by drawing their counters in each recording space.

Picture count
PAGE 12

Learning objective
To count objects which can be touched but not moved.
What to do
This is an activity for either a small group or for individuals. Ask children to cut out the picture and numeral cards. Invite them to count the pictures and find the matching numeral. Combine two sets of picture cards for pairs of children to play 'Snap' or 'Pelmanism'.

Snail trails
PAGE 13

Learning objective
To count physical movements.
What to do
This game can be played by one to four children. Use an ordinary dice if the children can count the spots. Alternatively,

write numbers on a blank dice. As the children play check that they move their counter on each time, rather than counting the square that the counter is on as 'one'. Let the children take a copy of the game home to play.

PAGE 14

Spot count

Learning objective
To count items which can be seen but not touched.

What to do
This is a dice game for one to four children. Use an ordinary dice with spots. Ask the children to take turns to throw the dice and to find the picture with the same quantity. Encourage them to count by looking, not touching. The less confident can touch to count. The more able children could use numeral cards instead of a dice.

PAGE 15

Count and match

Learning objective
To recognize quantities which are the same as each other.

What to do
Ask children to work in pairs. Give each pair a copy of the sheet and some coloured buttons or counters. Ask them to take turns to cover two pictures which have the same quantity of cats with the matching number of counters and check each other's accuracy of counting. The sheet can also be cut up and the pictures used for 'Snap' or 'Pelmanism' games. Use the sheet also for a game of 'Lotto', where you say a number and the children cover a picture of that quantity.

PAGE 16

Flower petal snap

Learning objective
To count items which can be seen but not touched.

What to do
This is a game for pairs. Enlarge the sheet to A3-size onto a sheet of card and colour it in before the picture cards are cut out. Store the completed cards in an envelope to be used again and again. Teach the children how to play 'Snap' or 'Pelmanism', encouraging them to count the petals on each flower by looking but not touching. Less

confident children may find it helpful to touch count. Let the children take home a set of 'cards' to play with a relative or carer.

PAGE 17

How many?

Learning objective
To use number language in context.

What to do
This is a dice game for a group of four. Each child will need a copy of the activity sheet and some pennies. The children take it in turns to throw the dice. For each throw of the dice they all count out that number of pennies onto the top money box. Ask them to put pennies into the second box, such as: put more/fewer pennies; put the same amount; put one/two more. For the last turn of the game they can draw the pennies onto the money boxes as a record of their understanding of the relevant number language. Return to the game over time, gradually increasing the amounts involved.

PAGE 18

Animal count

Learning objective
To use number language in context.

What to do
Work with a group of four children. Give each child a resource sheet, which can be enlarged to A3-size, some crayons, scissors and counters. Ask the children to read then trace each numeral before cutting them out. The game can be played in various ways. Here are some suggestions:
• Match the quantity in each picture with counters.
• Place the matching numeral beside the relevant picture.
• Write the correct numerals beside each picture.
• Make sets of counters which are the same/more than/fewer than each picture.

At the end of the game invite the children to draw their own sets of animals up to ten, or more, depending on individual abilities.

Matching

Count how many. Draw some flowers to match.

Who has more?

Count Tom's shells. Draw some shells so that you have more.

Count and count again

Count out _____ counters.

Put the counters into a space.

Count them again.

Choose a different space and count again.

Picture count

Count how many in each set.

Match a numeral card to each set.

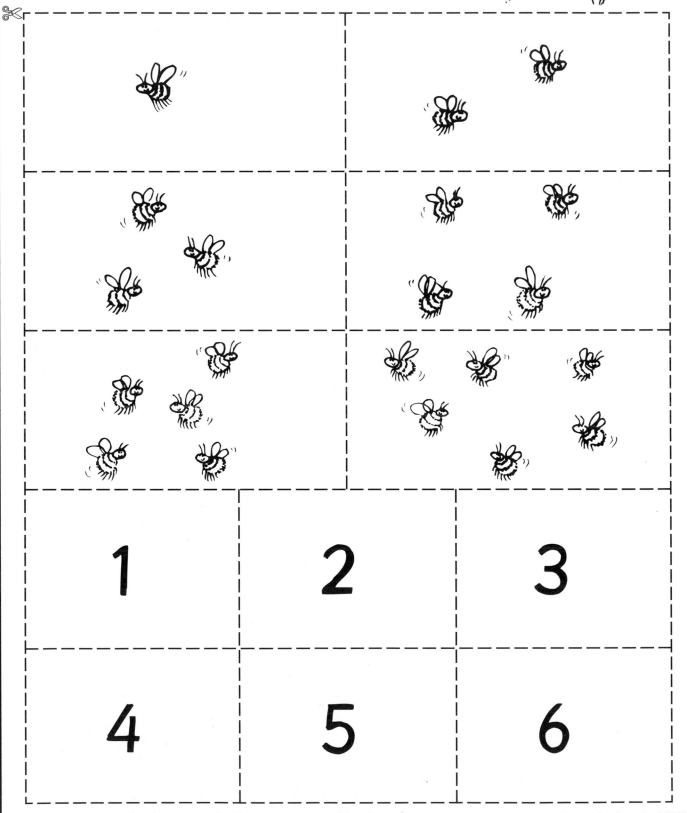

Snail trails

Put your counter on the snail.

Throw the dice.

Move your counter along to reach the lettuce.

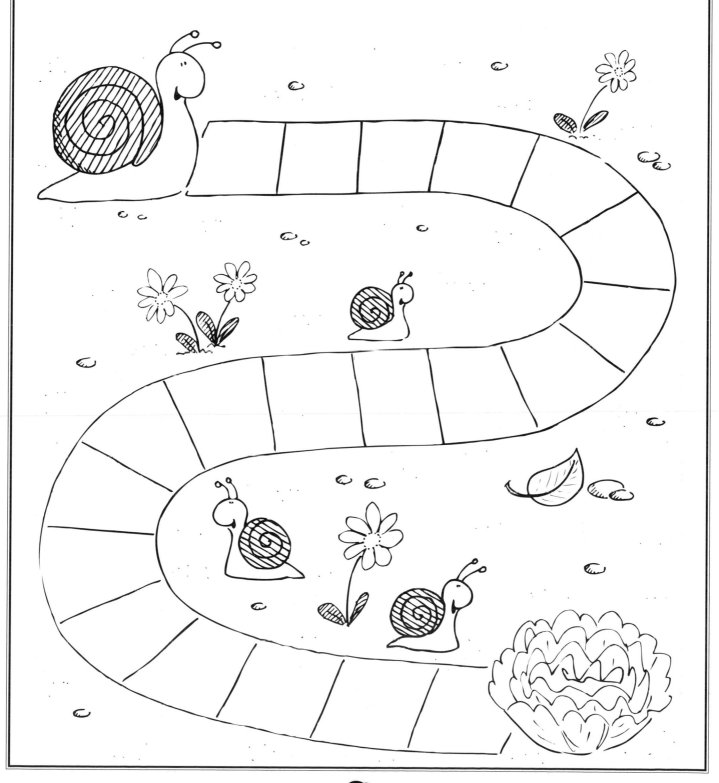

Spot count

Throw the dice and count the spots on it.

Find the picture with the same number of children.

Count and match

Make pairs of pictures with the same number of cats.
Put a counter on each cat. Count the cats.

Flower petal snap

Play snap. Count the
petals carefully.

How many?

Throw the dice. Put that number
of pennies in the cat money box.

Animal count

Trace over the numerals.

Count the animals. Match the sets

of animals with a numeral.

| 1 | 2 | 3 | 4 | 5 |

Learning in the Early Years - Photocopiable Activities

Mathematics

chapter two

Number

Use these ideas in conjunction with 'Chapter One – Counting' to help children to develop their ideas about number order, early addition and subtraction, sharing, and reading and writing numerals.

PAGE 21

Dotty pictures
Learning objective
To order numerals.
What to do
Work with a group of up to ten children. Provide each child with a numeral card, from 1 to 10, and ask the children to line up in number order. Less confident children can just use the numerals to 5. When the children are confident with the order of the numerals and can read them, ask them to complete the photocopy activity individually.

PAGE 22

Dotty numbers
Learning objective
To practise numeral formation 0 to 10.
What to do
Work with groups of four children and ask them to work in damp sand using their hands or spoon handles. Ask them to write each numeral from 0 to 10 in turn in the sand.

The activity sheet shows the shape and direction for writing the numerals 0 to 10. After the children have practised in the sand let them trace over the dots. Ensure that they are careful to form the numerals correctly, starting with the arrows.

PAGE 23

Number order
Learning objective
To recognize number order.
What to do
This is an activity for pairs. Enlarge the sheet to A3-size onto card. Let the children colour in the numerals and cut them out. Ask each pair of children to share a set and take turns to place the numerals in order, starting with 1, then 2 and so on. Let more confident children start with any numeral, such

as 3, then place 4, 5, and so on. For a group activity, spread the numerals out, face up, and ask: 'What number am I thinking of if it's between ... and ...?' or 'Which comes one before/after ...?' Invite the children to make up some games to play with the number cards.

Tea-party
PAGE 24
Learning objective
To count and find one more.
What to do
Work with a group of four children and give each child a plate and some counters. Say: 'Count five counters onto the plate. Make it one more/fewer. How many now?' For the more confident, ask for two more or fewer. Now give each child a copy of the sheet and ask them to cut out the pictures. Say: 'Show me the picture with five cakes. Which picture has one more/fewer?' Repeat both activities, using different starting numbers.

Snakes alive!
Learning objective
To count on and back.
What to do
Give each child in a group of four a counter and an activity sheet for this dice game. Ask the children to take turns to throw the dice, then to move their counter that number of spaces. Check that they count on and do not count the square where they previously landed. If they are correct, they can put another counter on a star. This game can also be played for counting back.

Snowman's buttons
Learning objective
To find different combinations to make using five.
What to do
Work with a group of four children. Put a saucer containing some buttons on the table and ask each child to choose five buttons. Ask them to put the buttons onto the snowman's waistcoat. Ask: 'How many on this side of the waistcoat? And on this side? How many altogether?' This can be repeated to find other ways of making five. As children become more confident they can repeat the activity over time for totals up to ten.

Dinner time
Learning objective
To make fair shares.
What to do
Give each child in a group of four a copy of the activity sheet and some counters as 'bones'. Ask the children to share six 'bones' between two dogs so that both have fair shares. Repeat this for other amounts. Discuss fair and unfair shares. Suggest that the children record for one of the quantities by drawing the bones in the bowls.

Ten and beyond
Learning objective
To name some larger numbers.
What to do
Use this game with a small group who are confident with counting, ordering and reading numerals beyond ten. Enlarge the sheet to A3-size and provide counters and a dice. The game is played like 'Snakes and Ladders', going up ladders and down hosepipes. Ask the children to say what number they land on each time.

Ladybirds
Learning objective
To record how many.
What to do
Give each child in a group of six a copy of the activity sheet and some counters. Say a number to write in the box under the first ladybird, such as four. Ask the children to put some counters onto the ladybird so that there are four dots in total. Let them draw spots to record the counters. Repeat for the other ladybirds.

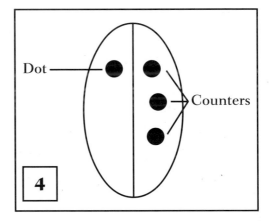

All about me
Learning objective
To use numbers in context.
What to do
Enlarge the activity sheet to A3-size. Work with groups of four children or send this sheet home with them. Give each child an activity sheet, some crayons and a pencil. Explain each part of the activity. Ask each child: 'How old are you? ... Draw that number of candles on the cake.' 'What is your house/flat number? ... Write the number on the door'. 'Who is in your family?... Draw them. Write down how many there are.'

Dotty pictures
Join the dots in order.

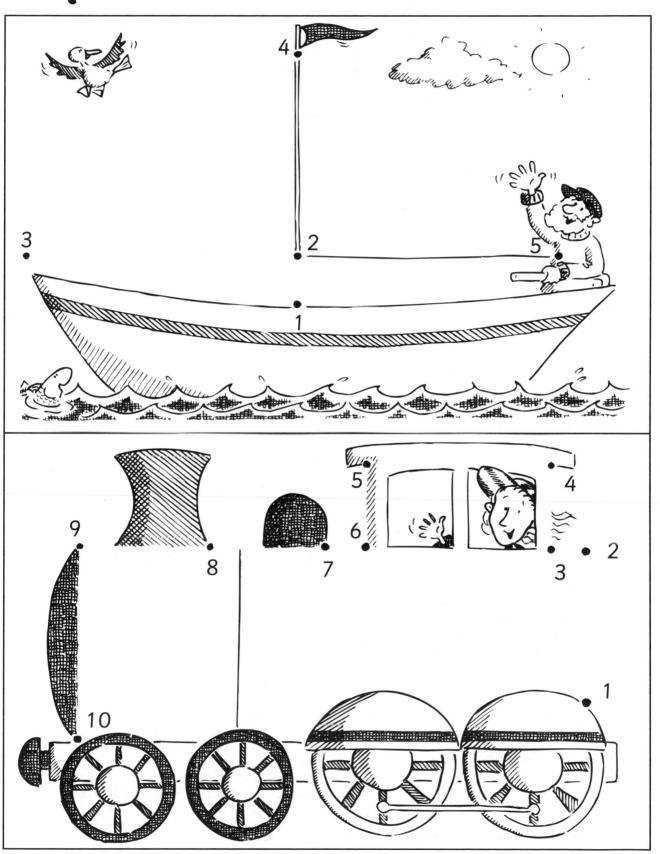

Dotty numbers
Follow the dots carefully.

Number order

Colour the
numerals and
cut out the cards.
Put them in order,
starting with 0.

3	6
7	9	4
5	1	10
8	0	2

Tea-party

Cut out the pictures. Put them in order from most to fewest.

Snakes alive!

Throw the dice. Move your counter along the snake.

Snowman's buttons

Put _____ buttons on the snowman's waistcoat.
Find different ways to place the buttons.

Dinner time

Put the counters on the bone.

Now give the dogs fair shares.

Learning in the Early Years - Photocopiable Activities

Mathematics

Ten and beyond

Put your counter on 'start'. Throw the dice and move the counter that number of places.

Ladybirds

Add more dots to the ladybirds to make the numbers.

Learning in the Early Years - Photocopiable Activities
Mathematics

All about me

My name is _____

I am _____ years old.

My front door number is _____

This is my family. There are _____ people.

chapter three

Pattern

These activities help children to describe patterns and to make their own. Practice at these activities will help to prepare children for making number patterns later on.

PAGE 33

Build an order
Learning objective
To describe an order.
What to do
Work with four children and provide each of them with buttons in two colours, a copy of the activity sheet and crayons. Put out two different coloured buttons. Ask: 'What colour is first? And next?' Put down a third button and ask the same questions. Ask children to make their own order of three or four buttons (using their two colours). Ask them to describe it. When they are confident let them complete the activity sheet. Challenge the more able children to make each row look different. Repeat the activity using three colours.

PAGE 34

Iced cakes
Learning objective
To make line patterns.
What to do
Work with a group of four children to make some cakes or biscuits. Spread some icing onto the cakes then let the icing dry. Ask the children to make line patterns on their cakes using 'icing pens' (available in a variety of colours from supermarkets). Ask: 'Will your pattern be a straight/curved/wavy line? Will it go up and down? Repeat the pattern on another cake.' When the cakes are finished ask the children to draw their chosen line patterns on the cakes on the activity sheet.

PAGE 35

Tile patterns
Learning objective
To copy a pattern.
What to do
Work with a group of four children and ask them to copy each pattern on the activity sheet using shape tiles in two colours. Discuss the order of the shapes, using 'next', 'before' and 'after'. Encourage more able children to pay attention to the criteria of shape *and* colour, while less confident children may concentrate on copying just the shapes of the pattern. Invite the children to colour the patterns on the sheet to match the shape tiles they have used. Complete the sheet by asking them to make up their own patterns.

Animal patterns

PAGE 36

Learning objective
To copy and extend a pattern.
What to do
Prepare your own copy of the activity sheet, colouring in identical animals the same colour, and cutting out the tiles. Work with groups of four children and decide whether they should colour in their animals before they cut them out. Show the children your tiles and make a 'cat, dog, cat, dog' pattern and ask them to copy this. Ask: 'What would come next? And next?' and encourage them to extend their pattern in this way. Make other repeating patterns with the tiles. Ask the children to record their work by sticking their favourite patterns onto some paper.

Pattern allsorts

PAGE 37

Learning objective
To create a pattern.
What to do
Provide a selection of pattern-making materials such as beads, buttons, sorting toys and coloured crayons. Work with a small group and ask each child to make a repeating pattern. Encourage the less able to copy the ideas on the sheet and the more able to make up their own. Discuss each child's pattern,

using 'same', 'first', 'next', 'before', 'after', and 'last'. Let them record their favourite pattern by drawing it onto the activity sheet.

PAGE 38

Patterns everywhere

Learning objective

To create a pattern from shapes and lines.

What to do

Ask a group of four children to work in the sand making patterns using shells, rakes, spades, forks, buckets and other containers. At first their patterns may be random. Show them the sheet and ask them to decide upon a pattern beginning from the sheet and to choose the resources to make their pattern. They can copy and extend their chosen pattern or adapt one from the sheet to create their own. Repeat this activity over time, encouraging the children to choose different pattern ideas.

PAGE 39

Staircases

Learning objective

To make an increasing/decreasing pattern.

What to do

Use interlocking cubes, number rods, or a selection of bricks for this activity for individuals, pairs or a small group. Make a staircase pattern and ask: 'What comes first? And next? What is special about this pattern?'

Encourage the children to copy the patterns from the activity sheet and invite more confident children to make up their own.

PAGE 40

Cyclic patterns

Learning objective

To recognize cyclic patterns.

What to do

Work with a group of four children using beads and laces. Make a simple threaded pattern such as in the picture, joining the ends together to make a bracelet. Ask the children to describe it. Encourage them to make the patterns shown on the sheet. Invite more confident children to colour in each

bracelet to show the repeating pattern. Complete the activity sheet by inviting children to draw their own bead pattern.

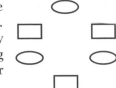

Tea-time

PAGE 41

Learning objective

To make patterns.

What to do

Use coloured counters in two colours and provide each of four children with a copy of the activity sheet. Explain that the counters are plates and cups that are to be placed around the tables. Ask the children to make a repeating pattern around the first table, using two of each colour for each chair. Repeat for the other tables. Encourage the children to describe each pattern by saying the colours, such as red, blue, red, blue, and to use words such as next, before and after. Invite them to colour in their repeating patterns on the sheet.

The fairground

PAGE 42

Learning objective

To recognize and describe linear and cyclic patterns.

What to do

Provide each child in a group of six with an activity sheet and coloured crayons. Ask: 'What patterns can you see? Find a stripy pattern. Find a zigzag pattern.' Ask the children to colour to make two or three colour repeating patterns (depending on their ability). Mount the completed activity sheets to include in a 'pattern display'.

Build an order

Make a pattern with some buttons. Colour these picture buttons to match.

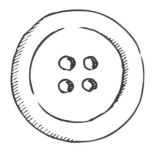 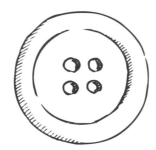 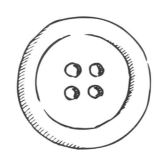 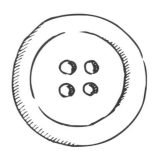

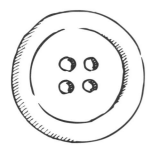 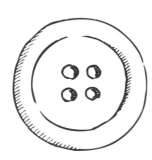 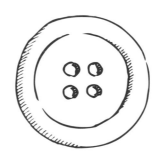 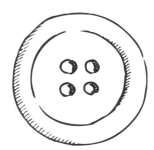

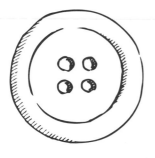 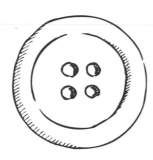 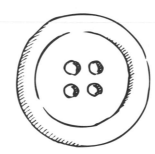 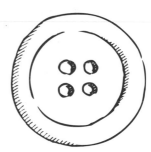

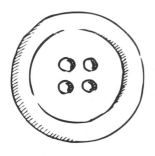 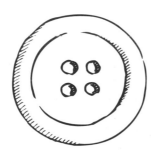 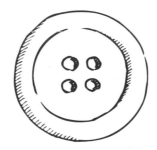 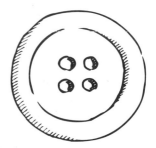

Iced cakes

Draw line patterns on these cakes.

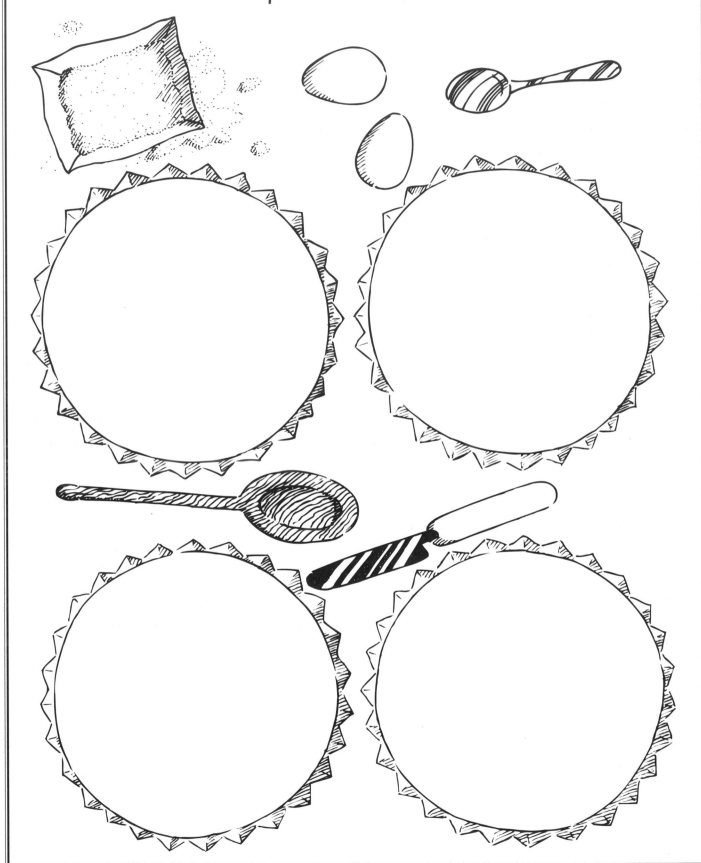

Learning in the Early Years - Photocopiable Activities

Mathematics

Tile patterns

Copy the patterns with tiles.

Make up your own pattern.

Animal patterns

Cut out the tiles. Make some patterns.

Pattern allsorts

This is Nathan's pattern.

  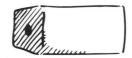

He used beads.

This is Naima's pattern.

She used toy cars.

This is Jade's pattern.

She used buttons.

Draw your best pattern here.

Patterns everywhere

Choose a pattern beginning.

Make your pattern in the sand.

Staircases

Copy these patterns.

Make your own pattern. Draw it here.

Cyclic patterns

Use some beads. Make these patterns.

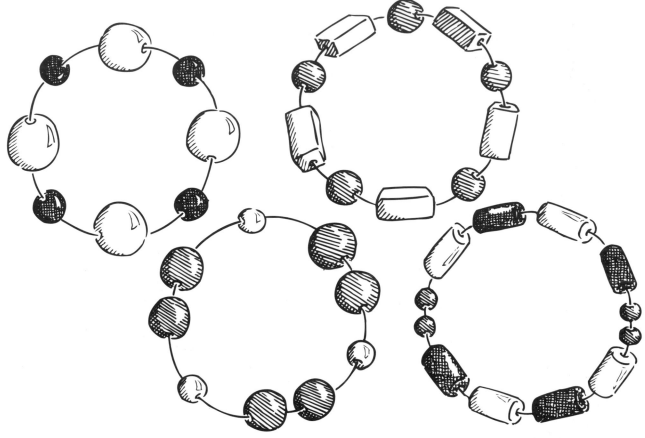

Draw your own bead pattern here.

Tea-time

Make a pattern at each table.

The fairground

Colour in to make repeating patterns.

chapter four

Sorting, matching and comparing

These activities will help children to begin to understand about measuring through sorting and matching, making comparisons and ordering.

Pair them up
Learning objective
To sort and match.
What to do
Work with a group of four children. Put some items which can be paired, such as socks, gloves, cup and saucer, into a shallow tray. Choose one item and ask: 'What goes with this? Why is that?' Repeat for the other items. Give each child a copy of the activity sheet and ask them to cut out the items. Invite them to pair these up and explain their choices before they stick the items in pairs onto some paper.

Longer and shorter
Learning objective
To use comparative language of length.
What to do
This activity is suitable for group, pair or individual work. Either place a range of everyday items of various lengths on a tray or ask the children to find items themselves in the room. Ask them to compare the items with the flower on the sheet and decide whether it is longer or shorter, then either place it or draw it in the appropriate set ring. Extend the activity with more confident children by asking them to find things that are 'about the same length'.

Which way home?
Learning objective
To make comparisons of length.
What to do
Enlarge one copy of the sheet to A3-size and work with the children individually. Ask them to find a way home on the sheet, pointing with their finger. Can they find a longer or shorter way? When the children are confident with the activity, give each a copy of the sheet and ask them to draw in a short and a long way home, using a different colour for each route.

Woof! Woof! Woof!

Learning objective
To sort objects and to order by length.
What to do
Prepare a copy of the sheet by colouring and cutting out the pictures. Ask a small group of children to sort the pictures into sets of 'the same' (bones, kennels and so on). Ask: 'Which is the longer bone, this one or that?' Put them in order, matching items under each other. Repeat for the other items. Now ask the children to give each dog their own bone, bowl and kennel, using words such as longer, shorter, taller, and wider. Give each child their own sheet and ask them to cut out, sort and stick the items onto some paper. Enlarge the sheet to A3-size for children with less-developed fine motor skills.

PAGE 49

The seaside

Learning objective

To use comparative language of weight.

What to do

Provide some items for weighing such as shells, pebbles, water, sand and a bucket balance. Work with a small group of children and ask them to put some shells into one bucket and balance it by pouring sand into the other bucket of the balance. Encourage children to say when the buckets are in balance. Ask: 'What happens if we put in more sand? More shells? Let's take some out. Now what happens?' Enlarge the activity sheet to A3-size and use it to reinforce and discuss the work. Ask: 'What can you tell me about the shells and the pebbles in the bucket balance?' (They are balanced, so weigh the same.) 'Which do you think is heavier, the sand pie or the bucket?' Use the sheet to discuss other comparisons of weight and let the children use the equipment to try out their ideas.

What happens next?

PAGE 51

Learning objective

To sequence events.

What to do

Work with a small group of children and sing the nursery rhyme 'Humpty Dumpty'. Give each child a sheet and ask them to cut out the pictures. Ask them to decide which is the first picture for the story, then the next and the next. Invite them to draw the end of the story. Encourage each child to tell the story including their ending.

Opposites

PAGE 52

Learning objective

To use comparative language of measures.

What to do

Ask the children to work with a partner to cut out the tiles from one activity sheet and pair pictures which show opposites. Ask them to explain each pair, using language such as long/short and narrow/wide. Encourage the more confident children to use comparative language such as longer and shorter. The tiles can also be used for games of 'Snap' and 'Pelmanism'. Let the children take the sheet home and explain to parents that you are encouraging the children to use comparative language.

PAGE 50

Marbles

Learning objective

To use comparative language of volume and capacity.

What to do

Put some water in a shallow bowl until it is almost full. Put the bowl on a tray to catch the overflow. Ask a small group to take turns to put a marble into the bowl until the water just spills. Ask: 'Is the bowl full/nearly full? How many more marbles do you think we shall need?' Empty the bowl and ask 'How much water is there now? How much shall we put in this time? How many marbles do you think we shall need to make the water spill? Now let's see.'

Pair them up

Cut out the pictures and match up the pairs.
Stick the pairs onto a piece of paper.

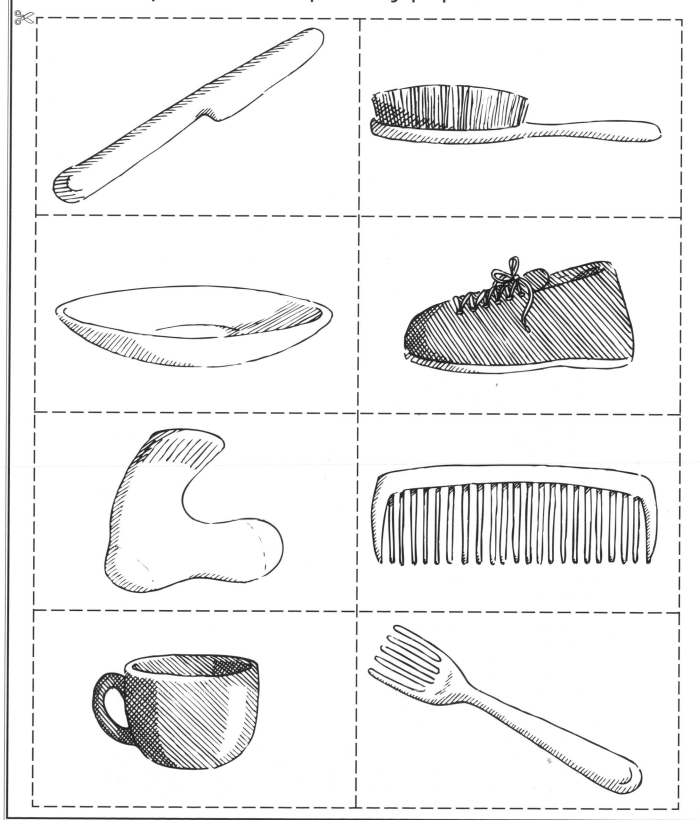

Longer and shorter

Find some things.

Sort them into longer and shorter than the flower.

longer

shorter

Which way home?

Find a short way home and a long way home.
Colour them in different colours.

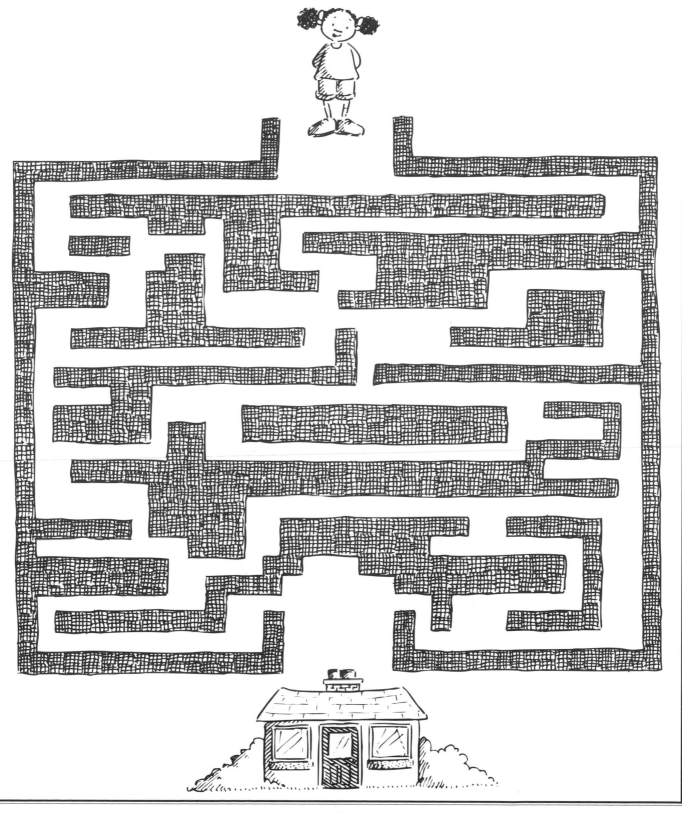

Woof! Woof! Woof!

Cut out the pictures.

Give each dog a bone, a bowl and a kennel.

Stick each set onto some paper.

The seaside

Look at the pictures and talk about making things balance. Try out your ideas.

Marbles

Put marbles into the water.

Find how many make the water spill.

Draw how many marbles you used.

What happens next?

Cut out the pictures and put them in order.

Draw a picture to finish the story.

Opposites

Cut out the tiles. Match up the opposite pairs.

chapter five

Shape and space

The activities in this chapter provide children with the opportunities to make models, play games and go for a 'shape walk' as they learn to use shape language to talk about what they can see and what they have made.

PAGE 55

Teddy twins
Learning objective
To recognize similarities and differences.
What to do
Copy the activity sheet and cut out a set of teddy tiles. Work with a group of four children. Choose two of the tiles and ask: 'Are these teddies the same? How are they the same? How are they different?' Now choose another two and ask the children to describe any similarities and differences they notice. Give each child a sheet and ask them to cut out the tiles and make sets of similar teddies.

PAGE 56

Shape difference
Learning objective
To recognize same and difference in shapes.
What to do
Work with a group of four children. Give each child a copy of the activity sheet, a pencil and some crayons. Explain to the children that the two pictures are nearly the same. Point to the lower picture and ask: 'What is different?' Ask the children to describe the differences that they spot and then draw in the missing lines. Let them colour the pictures so that they are both the same.

PAGE 57

Jigsaw match
Learning objective
To fit shapes together.
What to do
Copy the sheet onto card, enlarged to A3-size. Use the large jigsaw with pairs of children, asking them to take it in turns to fit the pieces together. Encourage them to use words such as next to, in front of and behind, as they work through the activity.

PAGE 58

Shape walk
Learning objective
To identify 3D and 2D shapes.
What to do
Work with groups of four children and provide each child with a copy of the sheet, a clipboard and a pencil. Explain that you are going for a shape walk (this can be inside or outside) and that everyone will be looking for shapes like those on the sheet. Discuss what each shape is called and look for examples together. As the children spot relevant shapes, ask: 'Is it round/straight/curved/flat?' Encourage the children to draw the objects inside the relevant shapes on their sheet.

PAGE 59

Behind the wall
Learning objective
To describe simple properties of 3D and 2D shapes.
What to do
Use a set of building bricks, and place a simple screen between two children. Ask the children to take four blocks so that they each have the same. One child makes a model behind the screen then describes to the other one how to make it. Encourage them to use words such as cube, cone, on top, beside and so on. Compare the models to see if they are the same. The activity sheet contains a similar activity using shape tiles.

PAGE 60

Face match

Learning objective

To recognize faces of 3D shapes.

What to do

Work with pairs of children. Enlarge the activity sheet to A3-size and provide a spot dice, two counters and a set of bricks with at least four of each shape to share between the children. Ensure that the children are familiar with the terms 'face, match and shape'. Show them a shape and ask: 'Which picture on the sheet does this face match?' Repeat for the other shapes.

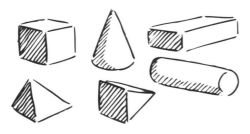

The children take turns to throw the dice and land on a space on the board. They find a brick which matches a face to the shape on the board space. They put the brick into the middle of the board. Play continues until all their shapes have been used.

PAGE 61

What is it?

Learning objective

To explore reflection and symmetry and develop the associated language.

What to do

Provide each child in a small group with a copy of the sheet and a safety mirror. Ask them to look at the half shapes on the sheet and guess what they are, then place their mirror on the line and look in the mirror. When they have recognised the shape ask them to complete the shape by drawing.

PAGE 62

Doll's house

Learning objective

To use language of position and movement.

What to do

Ask two children to work with you. Put some doll's bedroom furniture beside the doll's house and ask the children to put it into the bedroom using the sheet as a stimulus. Ask: 'What goes behind/ in front of/next to…?' Let more confident children draw their own doll's bedroom. Ask them to describe the position of their 'furniture'.

PAGE 63

Which way home?

Learning objective

To explore position and movement.

What to do

Give each of four children a copy of the sheet and some coloured crayons. Ask them to draw in a way home for the cat and then to describe it, using words such as turn and straight. Repeat for the other animals using different colours. Ask parents to work with their child at home to make up another maze or draw a simple map to show the way home from the group.

PAGE 64

Models

Learning objective

To interpret pictures.

What to do

Use this sheet as a starting point for making models. Help a small group to each try to make the robot. Encourage them to look at the picture to help them. Ask them to describe how they made their model. Let them choose another model to make.

Teddy twins

Cut out and make sets of teddy tiles.

Learning in the Early Years - Photocopiable Activities
Mathematics
TO29757

Shape difference

Find the differences.

Draw to make the pictures the same.

Jigsaw match

Cut out and make into a jigsaw.

Shape walk

Look for these shapes. Draw what you see.

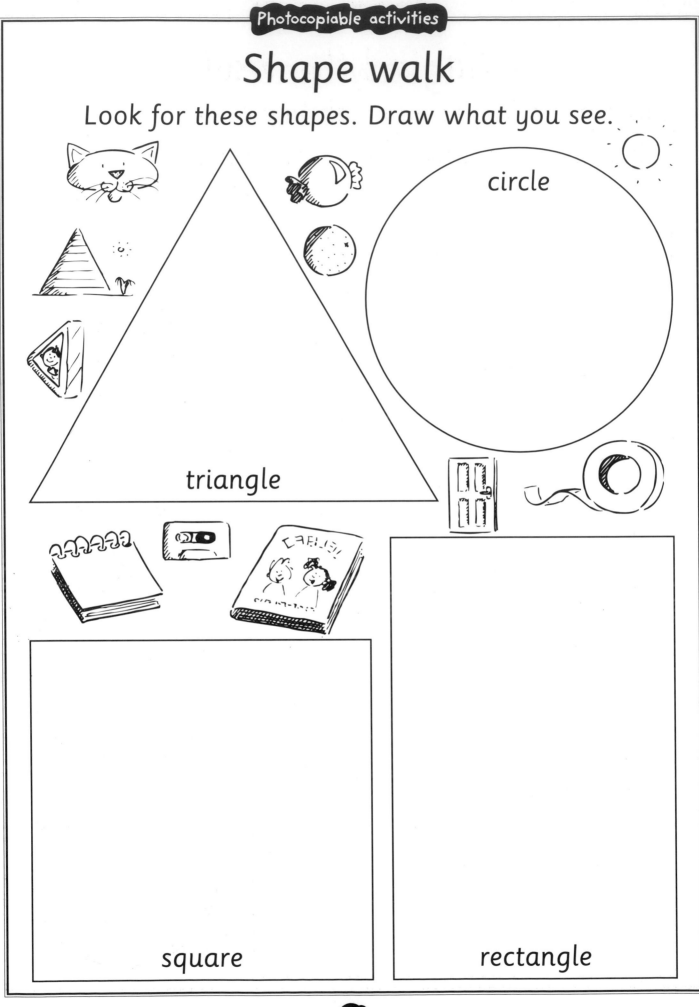

circle

triangle

square

rectangle

Behind the wall

Cut out the shapes and make a picture.

Tell your friend how to make one the same.

Face match

Throw the dice and
move your counter.
Find a brick that matches.

What is it?

Put the mirror on the line. What can you see?

Finish the picture.

Learning in the Early Years - Photocopiable Activities

Mathematics

Doll's house

Put some furniture in the doll's bedroom.

Learning in the Early Years - Photocopiable Activities
Mathematics

Which way home?
Draw the way home.

Models

Make these models.

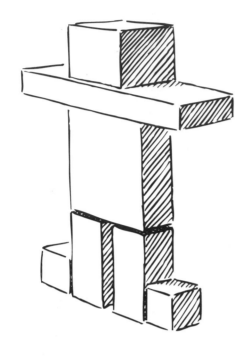

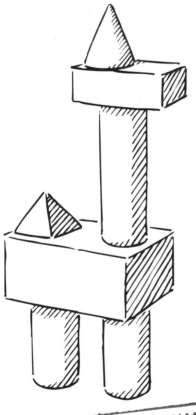